MAKING THE GRADE ·

EASY POPULAR PIECES FOR YOUNG CLARINETTISTS. SELECTED AND A

3

Published by
Chester Music
14-15 Berners Street, London, W1T 3LJ, England.

Exclusive Distributors:
Music Sales Limited
Distribution Centre, Newmarket Road, Bury St. Edmunds, Suffolk IP33 3YB, England.
Music Sales Pty Limited
20 Resolution Drive, Caringbah, NSW 2229, Australia.

Order No. CH78595

Music arranged and processed by Jerry Lanning.
Edited by Heather Ramage.
Printed in the EU.

www.musicsales.com

Chester Music
part of The Music Sales Group
London/New York/Paris/Sydney/Copenhagen/Berlin/Madrid/Tokyo/Hong Kong

MAKING THE GRADE · GRADES 1-3

GRADE 1-2

MAKING THE GRADE · GRADES 1-3

INTRODUCTION

This collection of 34 popular tunes has been carefully arranged and graded to provide attractive teaching repertoire for young clarinettists. The familiarity of the material will stimulate pupils' enthusiasm and encourage their practice.

The technical demands of the solo part increase progressively up to the standard of Associated Board Grade 3. The piano accompaniments are simple yet effective and should be within the range of most pianists.

Breath marks are given throughout, showing the most musically desirable places to take a breath.

ANY DREAM WILL DO

(from "Joseph and the Amazing Technicolor® Dreamcoat")

Music by Andrew Lloyd Webber. Lyrics by Tim Rice

Take care with the dotted rhythms. Keep the semiquavers light and try to match the accompaniment.

THE SKATER'S WALTZ

By Emil Waldteufel

Try to play the last eight bars in a single breath.

EENSY, WEENSY SPIDER

American traditional

You'll need to snatch a quick breath in bar 16. Don't be late on the second beat!

PAVANE

(from "The Capriol Suite")

By Peter Warlock

Try for a smooth, sustained sound, but be sure to tongue each note firmly.

I'M POPEYE THE SAILOR MAN

Words & Music by Sammy Lerner

This piece needs a bright and breezy performance!

EDELWEISS

(from "The Sound of Music")

Words by Oscar Hammerstein II. Music by Richard Rodgers

Play each phrase as smoothly as possible. Listen carefully to the tuning.

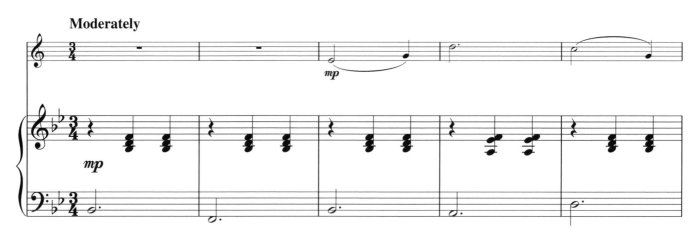

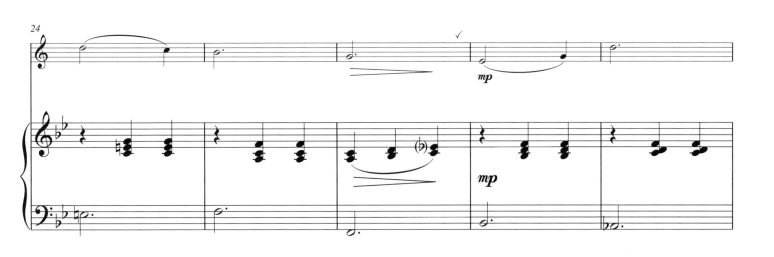

O NO, JOHN!

English traditional

Play the last four bars quite forcefully, for contrast.

SARABANDE

(from "Keyboard Suite IX")

By George Frideric Handel

In this piece it's probably best to breathe every two bars.

I HAVE A DREAM

Words & Music by Benny Andersson & Björn Ulvaeus

Make sure you always take a full breath, even though most of the phrases are short.

THE YELLOW ROSE OF TEXAS

American traditional

Play with a full sound, and make sure you tongue each note.

JEAN DE FLORETTE (THEME)

By Jean-Claude Petit

Take your breaths quickly, so that you don't have to cut the dotted minims too short.

NO MATTER WHAT

Music by Andrew Lloyd Webber. Words by Jim Steinman

Take care with the start of each phrase. It's very easy to be late!

HEY HEY ARE YOU READY TO PLAY

(Tweenies Theme)

Music by Graham Pike & Liz Kitchen. Words by Will Brenton & Ian Lauchlan

Listen hard to the tuning of the octave leaps. Keep the rhythm relaxed.

GUANTANAMERA

Music adaption by Pete Seeger & Julian Orbon. Words adapted by Julian Orbon from a poem by José Marti

Keep the rhythm very steady. When a phrase ends with a quaver, play the quaver lightly.

BARBIE GIRL

Words & Music by Soren Rasted, Claus Norreen, Rene Dif,
Lene Nystrom, Johnny Pederson & Karsten Delgado

Take a good breath on the first beat of bar 6, to carry you through to the end of the phrase.

THE PHANTOM OF THE OPERA

(from "The Phantom of the Opera")

Music by Andrew Lloyd Webber. Lyrics by Charles Hart. Additional lyrics by Richard Stilgoe and Mike Batt.

Be absolutely precise with the dotted crotchet/quaver rhythms.

LAND OF HOPE AND GLORY

By Edward Elgar

Try for a very smooth, sustained sound. Don't let the tempo drag.

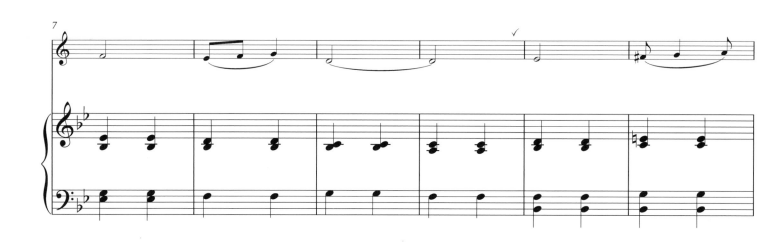

ALL MY LOVING

Words & Music by John Lennon and Paul McCartney

Be careful to read the rhythms carefully – don't guess!

SOMETHIN' STUPID

Words & Music by C. Carson Parks

Articulate the repeated quavers neatly and evenly.

31

OOM PAH PAH

(from "Oliver")

Words & Music by Lionel Bart

This piece needs a strong performance, but the middle section should be softer and smoother for contrast.

DANCE TO YOUR DADDY

English traditional

Accent the first beat of each bar slightly, but play the other notes quite lightly.

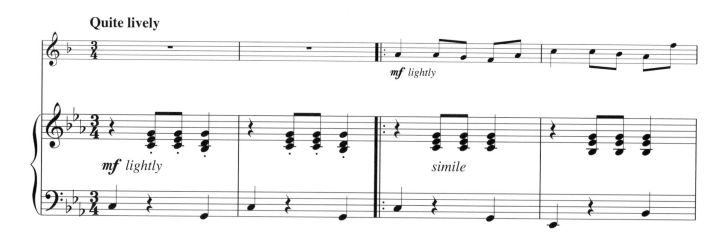

THE INCREDIBLE HULK (THEME FROM)

Composed by Joe Harnell.

This theme from the TV series is a wistful and attractive melody, which reflects the gentle side of the Hulk's nature.
Try not to cut any phrases short before you breathe.

YESTERDAY

Words & Music by John Lennon & Paul McCartney.

Most peoples' favourite Beatles song. Notice the C sharp and D sharp in the ascending scale of E melodic minor (bar 4), followed by the C and D naturals in the descending scale.

Moderately

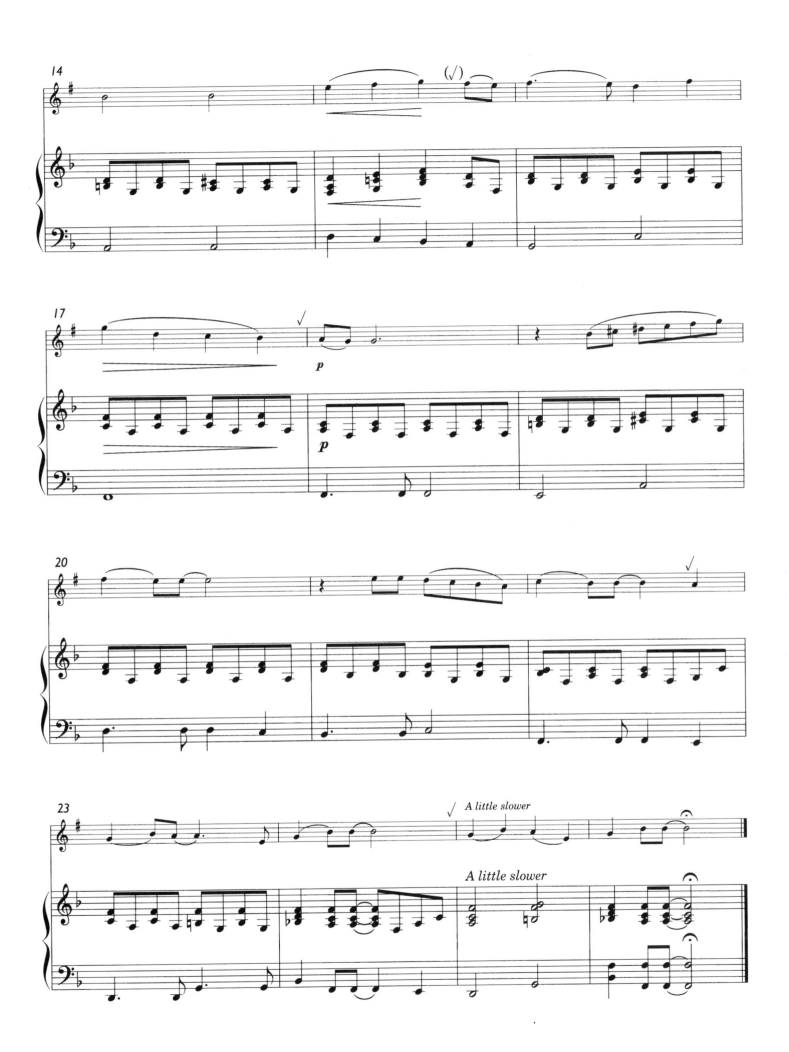

EL CONDOR PASA (IF I COULD)

Musical Arrangement by J. Milchberg & D. Robles. English Lyric by Paul Simon.

This is a traditional melody from South America, made popular by Simon and Garfunkel.
Keep a very steady tempo.

41

SUMMERTIME

Music by George Gershwin.

'Summertime' is probably Gershwin's most famous tune. The notes aren't difficult,
but be careful that you play the correct rhythm in bars 11 and 12. Don't let the final D go flat.

Moderately slow

ITSY BITSY, TEENIE WEENIE, YELLOW POLKADOT BIKINI

Words & Music by Lee Pockriss & Paul J. Vance.

If you want to leave out the spoken sections, you can cut from the first beat of bar 10 to the second beat of bar 12, and cut bar 22 completely. Watch out for the $\frac{2}{4}$ bar.

Two, three, four,

Stick a - round we'll tell you more.

45

BRIDGE OVER TROUBLED WATER

Words & Music by Paul Simon.

Here is Paul Simon's most enduring song.
Try for a full, rounded tone as the piece builds to a climax around bar 23.

Not too fast

I KNOW HIM SO WELL

Words & Music by Benny Andersson, Tim Rice & Bjorn Ulvaeus.

Many of the notes are slurred in pairs,

which should be practised carefully to ensure that the second note of each pair 'speaks' clearly.

BIRDIE SONG/BIRDIE DANCE

Words & Music by Werner Thomas & Terry Rendall.

Articulate the quavers in the first section clearly, almost *staccato*,
to contrast with the smoothly phrased second part.

JEANIE WITH THE LIGHT BROWN HAIR

Words & Music by Stephen Foster.

This song needs really expressive playing.
Be particularly careful of the slurred ninth (F to G) in bar 14. The G should be really soft.

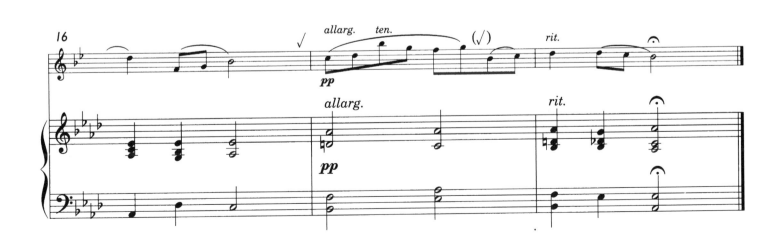

HE AIN'T HEAVY HE'S MY BROTHER

Words by Bob Russell. Music by Bobby Scott.

Some of the rhythms are a bit tricky in this piece. If you have some trouble with them,
practise each phrase slightly slower, counting in quavers. Be careful to count the rests in bar 21.

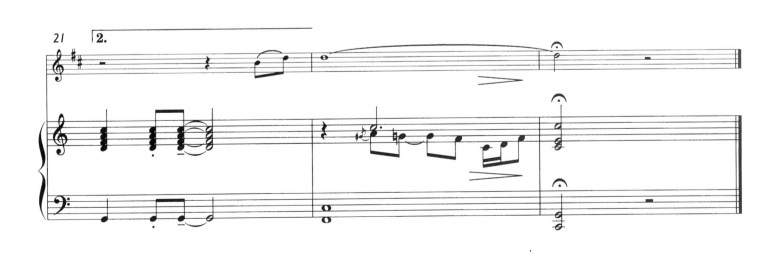

AMERICA

Music by Leonard Bernstein. Lyrics by Stephen Sondheim

In this lively number from 'West Side Story' the time signature alternates between $\frac{6}{8}$ and $\frac{3}{4}$;
you will need to keep this clearly in mind in bars 17 to 25.

BERGERAC

Composed by George Fenton.

Another TV theme, which here makes a substantial concert piece. The main theme is repeated an octave higher. Remember that D. 𝄋 al ⊕ Coda means 'Go back to the sign, then take the coda'.

Moderately bright

D. 𝄋 al
⊕ Coda

Coda ⊕

THE ENTERTAINER

By Scott Joplin.

This piano rag featured in the film 'The Sting'. Make sure you keep a very steady tempo.
You will find that the piece is quite a test of stamina.